C000040523

The Spider and the Bird

A play

Georgia Dobbs

Samuel French—London
New York-Toronto-Hollywood

ISBN 0 573 12259 8

Please see page iv for further copyright information

THE SPIDER AND THE BIRD

The Spider and the Bird was first presented at the Riverside Studios, London in December 1997 by the Rapscallion Youth Theatre, with the following cast:

Sonia	Polly Eachus
Spirit	Mindy Franklin
Nurse	Amy Tomkins
Peter	Roberto Viana
Margaret	Morgan Tovey-Frost
Mrs Farrow	Maggie Muldoon
Spud	Ore Sanderson
Debbie	Bella Baistow-Clare
Alex	Alex Smith
Carrot	Jonathan Gabb
Spider	Jamie Allan
Thug/Dingo	Mija Keadell
Thug/Policeman	Shaun Ricafranca
Thug/Policeman	Daniel Diedrick
Jamie	Ophelia Lovibond
Sarah	Keisha Murray
Pinch	Aurelia Allen
Josie	Dawn Brand
Loraine	Nadia Kamel
Spice	Rosie Mahoney
Tufty	Jason Federick

Directed by Georgia Dobbs

COPYRIGHT INFORMATION
(See also page ii)

CHARACTERS

Sonia's gang:
Sonia
Alex
Debbie
Carrot
Spud

Child, *Sonia's free spirit or angel*
Nurse
Margaret, *Sonia's mother*
Peter, *Sonia's father*

Pinch's gang:
Pinch
Loraine
Spice
Tufty

Jamie, *Pinch's brother*
Paul, *Jamie's friend*

Mrs Farrow, *headmistress*
Spider, *Harwood drug dealer*
Thug One
Thug Two
Thug Three
Dingo, *King Edward's drug dealer*

Policemen
School children

The number of characters in this play can be varied by adding extra gang
members. The sex of most of the characters can also be changed

DIRECTORS NOTES

This play was originally written to accommodate a large group of actors ranging in age from 8 to 18 years. As the children's availabilty during rehearsal was not always certain, the casting remained flexible. Therefore, extra characters can be easily added into either of the school gangs, Spider's mob or the school scenes. Actors may double as more than one character.

In the original production, the setting was kept as simple as possible. The hospital bed was set at the back of the stage. In scenes other than those set in the hospital, the bed was masked by a Venetian blind. In other scenes the Venetian blind was raised. Painted on one side of the blind was the Harwood School's emblem and the other side the King Edward's school emblem so that the blind could be opened revealing one or other of the two emblems. The blind was operated from the bed by the actress playing Sonia.

The front of the stage was mostly bare. Items of furniture were brought on to represent new scenes. For example, a bench for the playground and a table and cosy chair for the Gardner's living room.

Simple sound effects and lighting were used to help create the relevent scene and enhance an emotional state of a character.

Georgia Dobbs

Be like the bird, who
Resting in his flight
On a twig too slight
Feels it bends beneath him
Yet sings
Knowing he has wings.

Victor Hugo

THE SPIDER AND THE BIRD

SCENE 1

Late at night

The stage is dark and Techno music plays

On stage, unseen as yet, is a hospital room with a door to one side. There is a single bed. Next to the bed is a table, with a glass of water on it. There is bedside chair. The "fourth wall" is a window overlooking the hospital gardens

Spider and two of his thugs enter. They carry torches which only barely light the stage. They place themselves in three of the four corners of the stage, leaving the entrance free

After a moment, Sonia and her gang enter followed by a fourth thug. They are surrounded and try to run away. Each exit route is blocked, but Sonia's gang finally manage to run away

Sonia remains. She stands and stares at Spider. Spider and his thugs move towards her and pull her down to the ground. She is beaten up

The thugs leave the stage

Spider steps over Sonia's body and exits

The music begins to fade and is replaced by the regular sound of a heartbeat. We hear the faint sound of an ambulance. A red pool of light falls onto Sonia's body

A small child dressed in white enters and walks up to Sonia

The pool of red light turns to white

The child holds Sonia's hand and leads her to the hospital bed

The pool of light goes out and the heartbeat continues

SCENE 2

A hospital room

The heartbeat fades as the Lights come up

Sonia is asleep in the bed. The child dressed in white looks over her at the end of the bed

Nurse (*reading the doctor's notes from a clipboard*) Two broken ribs — bruising on the legs and face — traces of LSD in the patient's bloodstream. (*She pauses*) I've seen many like you in here. Saving your life is as rewarding as saving anyone else's. But you yourselves don't seem to think so. The way you drown yourselves in drugs and the way you fight and then arrive here in pieces, it's as though you put no value on your life. Sometimes I think I care more about your recovery than you do. I don't know why that is. Perhaps you think you have nothing to recover for. No sense of meaning or purpose in your life. That is what you are looking for isn't it, when you take these Ecstasy tablets or Acid trips, a reason to live? And if there's a high risk it doesn't matter because you don't yet have that reason. You aren't really doing anything criminal, only searching for a sense of meaning like the rest of us. Some turn to religion, some to politics, you turn to drugs. Only you won't find the answers there, you will only get more lost. So I hope you find something else to believe in, I really do, because drugs will kill you before they enlighten you.

Sonia stirs and slowly sits up

How are you feeling?
Sonia I'm not sure.
Nurse Here, take these. (*She hands Sonia some pills*)
Sonia No.

The Nurse puts them by the bed

Nurse Can you drink this? (*She hands her the glass of water*)

Sonia drinks

So, you want to live. That's good.
Sonia Be free.
Nurse What?
Sonia I had a dream. I feel strange.
Nurse You've been asleep for three days.
Sonia Three days?
Nurse Curtains open? (*She walks* DS *and mimes opening the curtains on the "fourth wall" window*)

Bright natural light comes in through the window and Sonia shields her face

Sonia Three days! What happened?
Nurse We've been waiting for you to tell us that.
Sonia What day is it?
Nurse Monday. You came in on Friday.
Sonia I had a strange dream. At least I think it was. I wish I could remember.
Nurse It'll come back to you. Your parents are outside.
Sonia Parents?
Nurse Yes.
Sonia Of course, I have parents.
Nurse Are you ready to see them?

Sonia I suppose that would be best.

The Nurse opens the door to leave

   Nurse?
Nurse Yes?
Sonia What is my name?
Nurse Sonia.

   The Nurse exits

Sonia Sonia. Sonia. Sonia.

   Sonia's parents, Margaret and Peter Gardner, enter

Peter Gardner does not greet Sonia. He walks DS and looks out of the window, into the audience. Margaret Gardner goes straight to Sonia and tries to embrace her. Sonia pulls back away from her mother's embrace

Margaret Sonia?
Sonia It's nice to meet you. I mean — er... What do I mean?
Margaret Sonia?
Sonia I mean, how have you been?
Peter Very clever.
Margaret Sh, Pete. She's not herself.
Sonia No, I'm not my usual self. I've been in an accident.
Peter Accident! You just can't stay out of trouble can you?
Margaret It isn't the right time for this, Peter.
Peter Look at her. She's a disgrace.
Margaret She's alive, isn't she? That's what counts.
Sonia Have I done something wrong?
Peter "Have I done something wrong?" ! You might fool your
   mother, but you don't fool me.
Margaret Peter!

Sonia Whatever it is I've done, I'm sorry.

Peter "Sorry!" I think that's the first time I've heard you use that word. Surprised you know what is means.

Sonia Well, you see, Peter — er ... Do I call you Mum and Dad or ...

Peter I've had enough of this great pretence. I know what you're like. You can't pull the wool over my eyes. I'm going before we both go completely soft.

Margaret Peter!

Peter Well, how many more times must I be humiliated, and by my own daughter? I'll be in the car, Margaret.

Peter exits

Margaret He doesn't mean to be so harsh. It's his work. You know how important it is to him. He's a proud man. He can't bear going into the station and hearing from his colleagues that you've broken the law again.

Sonia Do I break the law?

Margaret Let's not talk about it now. When you're well again. The nurse said you may be having trouble thinking clearly, but that you'll soon be as right as rain. I'll go and find your father now. You get some rest. I'll come straight back. If I find you asleep, I'll come back this evening and see if you're feeling any better. Get some rest. (*She kisses Sonia on the forehead*)

Margaret exits

Scene 3

On stage, L, are a teacher's desk and chairs

An assembly of school children gather, chat and fool around

Their headmistress enters and silences them

During the following the children may make comments and give reactions throughout the headmistress's address. She may add the occasional "Quiet!" or glare them to silence before continuing

Mrs Farrow Over the weekend I was informed that arrangements have now been finalized for Harwood High School to join with King Edward's next year. A decision has been made to extend the premises of Harwood and close King Edward's altogether. At first I was delighted that something is at last definite. However, it does mean, more strongly than ever, that the eternal feud between Harwood and King Edward's will have to stop. Anyone who continues to behave as though we are at war with the King Edward's pupils will be suspended if not expelled. Now, it is exactly fifteen months before you will be sharing classrooms with your enemies. I suggest you all make it your priority to make peace with them before that happens. My second point refers to the apparent profusion of drugs at Harwood. Yet again, I am forced to address this problem. It is my utmost priority to bring it to an end. Your form tutors will be talking to you in the course of this week. I hope you will listen carefully to what they have to say and take the matter very seriously indeed. What with all the brawling and drug taking I have been visited by the police thirteen times already this year. Thirteen times. I do not want you to give them any reason to come back to me again. If you all put as much effort into learning as you do offending, I would have a school full of grade A students. I will leave you to ponder that thought. Meanwhile, can I see Woods, Jones, Fithe and Roberts in my office please, immediately.

The assembly disperses and exit

Debbie, Spud, Carrot and Alex remain on stage

Spud I knew this would happen. My mum's going to kill me.
Debbie Just leave all the talking to me and Alex and we'll be fine, OK?
Spud What are we going to say?

Alex *You* say nothing.
Carrot Not a word.

Spud shows she is buttoning her lips

Alex Good. Ready, Debs?
Debbie Yup.

They knock on an imagined door to Mrs Farrow's office

Mrs Farrow Come in. Sit down.

They enter the office and sit down

I presume you know why you are here?
Alex No, Miss. We were wondering, Miss.
Mrs Farrow You were with Sonia Gardner on Friday evening. Is that correct?
Alex ⎫
Debbie ⎭ (*together*) Yes, Miss
Mrs Farrow Sonia is now in hospital. I want to know what happened to her.
Alex It was the bike shed, Miss.
Mrs Farrow The bike shed?
Debbie Sonia left her bike in the bike shed.
Alex We had to go back and get it that night.
Debbie Picture the scene, Miss. Sonia is on her way home, after a hard day at school, all ready to get down to doing her homework as soon as she gets in, when she suddenly realizes she has left her bike in the bike rack at school. So we all turned back with her to get it.
Alex It was *so* annoying.
Debbie As she was pulling it out of the rack, Miss, the whole thing fell on top of her.
Mrs Farrow Indeed?
Alex Three bikes had been left in the rack you see, Miss.
Debbie Big bikes.

Alex Mountain bikes.

Debbie And there was poor Sonia lying under three mountain bikes and a bicycle rack.

Carrot Squashed.

Spud Yeah.

Debbie Barely breathing.

Alex She's lucky to be alive, Miss.

Mrs Farrow Is she?

Alex Yes, Miss.

Mrs Farrow And we are lucky to have a bicycle rack still in its usual position, in the bicycle shed, where it has always been.

Debbie We managed to put it back you see.

Carrot Before helping her to the hospital.

Alex Only halfway there she fainted.

Carrot Collapsed.

Alex It was a tragic moment, Miss.

Mrs Farrow Yes. Most unfortunate. Most unfortunate that I wasn't there to have witnessed what really happened. However, I understand that Sonia is now fully awake and able to tell her version of the incident. I will be visiting her in hospital tomorrow, after which time I will know who will be receiving a detention, who will be suspended and who will be expelled. Have I made myself clear?

Alex
Debbie } (*together*) Yes, Miss.
Carrot

Mrs Farrow Good. It's half past nine. You better get to your classes. I'll be speaking with you again in the next few days.

All Yes, Miss.

Alex, Debbie, Spud and Carrot leave the office and remain outside

Debbie I don't believe it!

Carrot What are we going to do now?

Spud My parents are going to kill me.

Carrot I'm going to be banned from watching TV. I'll miss *EastEnders*.

Spud I'll tell you what's happening.

Carrot Thanks.

Alex We have got to tell Sonia what we've said to Miss Farrow. Otherwise our stories won't be consistent. I can't see her before tomorrow. I'm baby sitting my little sister.

Debbie Well I can't go. It's my Karate night.

Alex You two will have to go.

Spud I promised I'd be in tonight. They said they wanted to keep an eye on me.

They all look at Carrot

Carrot Don't look at me. I've been given detention all this week for the prank I played in the science lab, remember?

Debbie Somebody has to go.

Carrot I can go first thing tomorrow morning. I never turn up for woodwork anyway.

Alex Tomorrow it is then.

Debbie Don't forget, Carrot.

Spud I'm late for maths. Mr Layton'll kill me.

Carrot Spud. Wait for me.

They exit

SCENE 4

The hospital room

Sonia is in the room. The small child in white is sitting on the bed

Carrot enters

Carrot Sonia! Sonia!

Sonia Hallo. Who are you?

Carrot It's me. Carrot. Boy, they really laid into you didn't they?

Sonia They?

Carrot Look, I know what you are going to say and I'm really sorry.

Sonia About what?

Carrot I feel terrible about it and you're right. We let you down, badly.

Sonia What happened?

Carrot I know. We should never have deserted you like that. It's unforgivable.

Sonia Would you please tell me what happened.

Carrot Fear, Son, fear. They were bigger than we were. We got scared and ran.

Sonia From who?

Carrot Spider.

Sonia A spider?

Carrot No, stupid. Spider and his thugs. You mean you've been in here for three days and you haven't once thought of Spider?

Sonia No. Not once.

Carrot That's not like you.

Sonia Isn't it?

Carrot You meet him at the gates every other day.

Sonia What for?

Carrot For drugs, what do you think?

Sonia Do I take drugs?

Carrot Do I take drugs! Are you serious?

Sonia Are you?

Carrot Boy, they really laid into you.

Sonia I take drugs with you and a man called Spider who did this to me, is that right?

Carrot Not with Spider, no. With Alex, Debs and Spud. And me. We're in your gang.

Sonia And Spider?

Carrot Spider is our school's dealer. Harwood is his site. You must remember that?

Sonia Why?

Carrot Why what?

Sonia Why do we take them?

Carrot Why?

Sonia Yes why? What is it?

Carrot You seem — strange.

Sonia I'm trying to understand, Carrot. Is that right? I can barely remember you. I can barely remember myself. All I know is that I've woken up in a hospital. And I am being told that I am this misguided person who has lost her way.

Carrot Don't worry, Son. Your mates will put you back together again.

Sonia I'm not so sure. (*She gets out of bed and goes over the window*)

Sonia Carrot?

Carrot Yes.

Sonia Look at this.

Carrot What.

Sonia It's a bird's nest. It's got one, two, three chicks in it.

Carrot Oh yeah. Look at their scrawny necks. They look prehistoric.

Sonia They're so noisy.

Carrot And seriously ugly.

Sonia Just imagine, those tiny things are going to be birds one day. They will grow up and fly the nest. They'll be free. They'll live a natural life. You won't find them hurting each other or themselves. They'll respect the gift of life.

Carrot You are different.

Sonia I nearly died.

Pause

Spider enters with three thugs

Carrot Spider! Quick, Son, let's get out of here.

Sonia So you are Spider.

Carrot tries to slip past Spider and out of the door without being noticed

Spider In a hurry?

Carrot Ah, Yes! (*To Sonia*) Come on!

Carrot exits

Sonia doesn't move

Spider Feeling better Sonny?

Sonia Much better thank you. How are you?

Spider Are you trying to be funny?

Sonia No.

Spider Good. Because if you laugh at me, I'll break your scrawny little neck. Now, I am here to make you a proposition. Since our "discussion" on Friday evening, I have been doing some serious thinking. Which is more than I can say for some around here. (*He glares at the thugs*)

The thugs immediately straighten up. But, during the following they begin to wilt and slouch

Not everyone is adept in the ability to think. I am one of the few who are. Now, where was I?

Thug One Proposition.

Spider Yes, proposition. I don't like beating the life out of you, Sonny. You are too young to be laid out covered in bruises.

Thug Three Or earth.

Spider Or earth. I don't really want to kill you. I would rather have you look upon me as your protector, let's say, or mentor. You see, you have been one of my most loyal customers over the past year or so and I have now come to the conclusion that, although you have crossed me, I must be merciful. I am going to make you an offer. Provide you with an opportunity.

Sonia How have I crossed you?

Spider You, Sonny, have been dealing on my site. Harwood school is my site. No-one from outside or inside the school is to deal on my site. Everybody knows that. I'm already having to respond to a take-over threat from that poxy King Edward's dealer.

Thug Two Dingo.

Spider Yes, Dingo. So I don't need competition from you. That is why I have found it in my heart to be extremely generous. I have decided to turn a blind eye to your foolish behaviour and to see in you the potential for a trainee. Come into my web, Son, and I will help you grow big and fat.

Sonia Big and fat ...

Spider Power, Sonia! A person does not get many opportunities for power in a lifetime. Just you try setting up on your own. You'll soon learn how hard it is.

Sonia I don't want to be a ——

Spider Don't play the fool with me. Is it a deal or not?

Sonia No. No deal. I don't even want your drugs any more.

Spider You don't want ... No, I know you, Sonny, it won't last. Let's just say you've had a difficult few days surviving your punishment and now you want go straight. I understand that. I have seen it happen before. But you'll be back.

Sonia No. I won't. I'm clean, cleansed. Thank you very much for the opportunity of coming into your web and growing big and fat and all that, but it seems to me that I've been provided with another opportunity. I can let go of all the mess I've been caught up in if I want to. And I do want to. So don't worry about me dealing on your site because I won't be anywhere near it from now on. That's guaranteed!

Spider You're not feeling yourself, Sonia.

Sonia I am feeling myself. More than I have ever felt before in my whole life.

Spider But you've been showing such promise. (*Directed at the thugs*) Which is more than I can say for some around here.

The thugs straighten up at his glare

Not every one can spot talent, but I am one of the chosen few who can. You, Son, are a natural. Why throw a talent like yours away?

Sonia Me? I would be rubbish at it. I'd tell everyone to leave off taking drugs and be free to enjoy life without them. Be free. That's it. I remember my dream now.

During the following, as Sonia remembers the dream, the Lights fade a little and a spot comes up. Sonia steps forward into the spot light

I was caught up in a net. It was thick and ropy and the more I struggled with it, the more it tightened around me. Through the gaps in the rope I could see glimpses of the grass and the trees and the sky. When I focused on what I could see through the gaps, the net began to loosen and fall away until I was standing there, free, surrounded by nature.

Pause

Spider Have you lost it?

The Lights return to normal

Thug Two What's she talking about?
Sonia Don't you see? We've been concentrating on the wrong things.
Spider No I don't see. I see that you're concussed. I'll have to repeat my offer when you have fully recovered.
Sonia I'm not going to change my mind.
Spider You're being very foolish. I only ever give one chance to take an opportunity like this one and I ——
Sonia Sh. Listen.

They all listen. The sound of a fiddle being played in the street can be heard

It's a fiddle.

Sonia goes to the window

Thug One I know that one. My old man used to whistle it all the time.

Thug Two   (*singing*) Daisy, Daisy ——
Thug Two
Thug Three } (*together*) — give me your answer do.
                    I'm half crazy, all for the love of you ——
Thug One
Thug Two   }   — It won't be a stylish marriage.
Thug Three   'Cos I can't afford a carriage.
                    But, you'll look sweet,
                    Upon the seat,
                    Of a bicycle made for two.

They fall about laughing

Spider That's enough. Shut it!
Thug Three I know another version of that.
Thug One The rude version.
Thug Two Oh yeah.
Thug One
Thug Two   } (*together, singing*) Daisy, Daisy, isn't it plain to
Thug Three   see ——
Spider I'll throw the whole bleeding lot of you out of this window,
    if you don't shut it.
Thugs Yes, boss. Sorry, boss.

Spider leans out of the window

Spider (*shouting*) Oi! Shut it will you. You sound like a bleeding
    screeching tire. There are people trying to make a recovery in
    here. How do you expect them to do that with that racket going
    on outside their bleeding window?

The sound of the fiddle stops

    (*He turns back into the room and looks at Sonia*) *You* are trouble.
    Now, are you or are you not going to come on board?
Sonia No.

    Margaret and Peter Gardener enter. Margaret carries a box of biscuits. She sits down next to the bed. Peter remains at the door and studies Spider. Spider notices and stares back at him

Margaret Oh, you've got visitors. We're not interrupting anything I hope.

Sonia No. Our conversation had just finished.

Margaret Well, won't you introduce us then?

Sonia No, you see, I don't really know them, I mean, I used to but now we are going our separate ways. In fact they were just leaving, weren't you?

Margaret That's not very polite, Sonia. They have come to see you. I'm sure they have been as concerned for you as we have.

Spider Indeed we have, Mrs Gardner. Indeed we have.

Margaret How do you do?

Spider Delighted to make your acquaintance.

Margaret Now, did you sleep well?

Sonia Yes.

Margaret You're looking much better, isn't she Peter ?

Peter gives no response

I hear your appetite is back. The nurse said you ate breakfast. I made some biscuits if anyone would like one. (*She opens the box and puts it on the bed*)

Sonia takes a biscuit

Thug One Don't mind if I do. (*He takes a biscuit, bites into it, realizes it's delicious and takes the whole box over to the other thugs*)

Sonia They're delicious.

Thug Two Ginger, my favourite.

Spider grabs the box of buscuits from the thugs. He glares at the thugs as they stuff their faces. Then, he takes a buscuit himself and returns the box to Margaret. He smugly bites into his buscuit, while looking straight at Peter

Margaret Peter? (*She offers Peter a biscuit*)

Peter Don't be ridiculous. Who are these people, Sonia?

Spider Let me introduce myself. I am known in these parts as Spider and these are my followers. (*He looks at the thugs*)

The thugs are tucking into their biscuits

Peter Yes, I have heard the name before. Remind me what it is you do.

Spider I am, let us say, a therapist of sorts in these parts.

Peter Therapist!

Spider Yes. I analyse peoples problems and then suggest a solution. I tend to be very effective in suggesting the right thing.

Peter Is that so?

Spider Yes.

Margaret That sounds very interesting. Peter here is a policeman.

The thugs choke on their biscuits and head for the door to make a hasty exit. Thug One stuffs his pocket with biscuits before leaving

Spider Fascinating line of work, however I think we better be going. Later, Son.

Thug Three (*with his mouth full of biscuit, to Margaret*) Delicious biscuit.

The thugs exit

Spider walks to the door to exit. Peter stands in front of the door for a moment and takes a good look at Spider

Peter So glad to put a face to the name.

Spider exits

Peter Good-for-nothings. You are an embarrassment to me. I ought to hand you in..

Margaret Are they friends of yours?

Sonia No. It's like I said. I did sort of know them, but not any more.

Margaret Oh.

Peter You may fool your mother, but you don't fool me.

Sonia So you said before.

Margaret I'm sure Sonia's not trying to fool anyone, Peter.

Peter We'll see. We'll see how long it is before the next lot of trouble. I'm on duty tonight. I'll have to look the chief constable right in the eye. Not that easy any more.

Margaret Pride, Sonia. That's all it is. I know how much he loves you. Even if he can't bring himself to say it.

Peter ignores her. He stares out at the window, but is still listening

You will try and stay away from the trouble makers though, won't you?

Sonia Yes, I intend to.

The Nurse enters

Nurse I'm sorry to cut your visit short, Mr and Mrs Gardener, but I'm going to have to ask you to leave. We've got her on a strict course of medication and rest.

Margaret I understand.

The Nurse exits

Tomorrow, it seems, we can take you home. You'll be back in your own room again.

Sonia My room. Yes. I remember that as well now.

Margaret looks at Peter

Peter I've got nothing to say.

Margaret God Bless.

Margaret switches off the light as she heads for the door

Margaret and Peter exit

The Light from the window falls into the room

Sonia My room. I'll see my room, with the ceiling I painted black and covered in glow stars. My Snoopy pillow case needs mending. Those horrible beige tiles in the bathroom. The living room with all Mum's old housekeeping manuals lying around. The kitchen where Rocky always tries to fit through the cat flap. I'll see my school and my mates. Carrot, Alex, Spud, Debs. That picture that Carrot drew on my desk of his ideal woman. Mr Jeffries. Mrs Farrow. I remember everything. I remember who I am, who I was, who I am now.

SCENE 5

King Edward's school playground

Jamie and Paul are on stage

Pinch enters and waits for his gang members to arrive. During the following, the others arrive one by one until only Tufty is missing

Paul Hey, Jamie. Your brother's over there.

Jamie Oh yeah. Dead cool, isn't he? Listen right. I met this guy the other day called Spider. Pinch knows him. He said he could get us some drugs.

Paul There's a few of them around. This weirdo, called himself Dingo, started talking to me at the bus stop. He went on and on about how great they were.

Jamie Dingo, yeah, I've heard of him.

Paul Really creepy, he is.

Jamie Anyway I asked him to get me some.

Paul No way. Jamie, they're really bad for you. They can even kill you. I was reading about them in the ——

Jamie Pinch has taken them and nothing happened to him.

Paul So? He was lucky.

Jamie Spider told me you'd say that. I'm going to try them anyway. They sound dead cool.

Paul You're mad.

Paul exits

Jamie follows Paul and passes Pinch on his way

Pinch All right, Jamie.
Jamie Oh. Hi, Pinch.

Jamie exits. Tufty runs on and joins the gang

Pinch Hurry up, Tufty. You're late.
Tufty I was fixing my hair.
Loraine Of course. What else?
Tufty Hey, when you are as good looking as I am, your hair is no small consideration.
Loraine Whatever.
Spice Why are we having this meeting, Pinch?
Pinch We need to talk about the merge with Harwood next year.
Tufty Oh that.
Loraine We mustn't let them think that we're going to play the underdogs just because we are on their territory.
Pinch Exactly.
Tufty So what are we going to do?
Pinch I want to challenge Sonia's gang to a fight. Whoever wins takes leadership at Harwood.
Spice Does that mean we have to fight Carrot?
Pinch Yes. All of them. That way we're letting them know that we won't be pushed around.
Tufty Or picked on.
Loraine Or bullied.
Spice OK. I get it!
Tufty Where's it to be? The boatyard?
Spice Someone will see us.
Loraine Not if it's late.
Pinch Ten p.m. at the boatyard, on Friday night.
Tufty I was going to have my hair trimmed on Friday. It'll get all messed up.
Loraine Life is so hard!
Pinch Are we agreed?
All Agreed.

Pinch Tufty, you can go and tell the Harwood lot.
Tufty Why me?
Loraine Just do it.

They exit

Scene 6

Harwood School

Alex, Carrot and Spud enter

Alex Well? Did you tell her?
Carrot Tell her what?
Spud Carrot! You were supposed to warn her about Mrs Farrow's visit.
Carrot Oh that. No. I didn't get a chance.
Spud ⎱
Alex ⎰ (*together*) Great!
Carrot I couldn't help it. I was going to tell her, but Spider turned up.
Alex Spider?
Carrot Yeah. I wasn't going to hang around while he was there. But it didn't seem right anyway. There was something weird about her.
Spud She's always weird. That's her style.
Carrot Something too normal about her then. I don't know. She was different.
Spud Give us an example.
Carrot She's forgotten things. She didn't even know who I was. She didn't know what had happened to her. And when Spider walked in she was completely fearless.
Spud Fearless of Spider?
Carrot He was in her room for ages talking about something. I looked through the curtain on the door and she was chatting away as if it was one of us she was talking to. If anything Spider looked more threatened than she did.

Spud He didn't hurt her then?
Carrot Nope.

Debbie enters

Debbie Tufty from King Ed's was at the school gates just now.
Carrot Was Spice with him?
Debbie No, why?
Carrot No reason.
Debbie Pinch's gang want to fight us.
Alex On what grounds?
Debbie To decide who takes leadership when the schools merge.
Spud Sonia's our leader and we lead the school. Right?
Carrot Right, Spud!
Debbie It's at the boatyard. Ten p.m. on Friday night.
Carrot (*sarcastically*) Great!
Spud What about Sonia?
Alex I'll go and see her now. I'll tell her about it.

Debbie and Alex exit

Carrot Damn!
Spud What's up, Carrot?
Carrot Oh nothing.
Spud Why did you want to know if Spice was at the school gates?
Carrot Spice?
Spud Yeah.
Carrot Spice who?
Spud Spice who! Spice from Pinch's gang. You fancy her, don't you?
Carrot No.
Spud Yes you do. I can tell. Woman's intuition.
Carrot Drop it!
Spud You can't fancy someone from Pinch's gang or someone from King Edward's for that matter. It's just not done. That's a double sin you're committing.

Carrot I haven't said I do fancy her.

Spud Yeah, but I can tell.

Carrot You say anything to anyone Spud and I'll tell your mother what you get up to when you're not at home.

Spud I knew it. Carrot fancies a Teddy's girl. Carrot fancies a Teddy's girl.

Carrot Spud! Spud!

Spud skips off stage. Carrot runs after her

SCENE 7

The hospital room

Sonia and the child in white are sitting on the bed. Mrs Farrow is sitting by the bed

Mrs Farrow And your memory has fully returned?

Sonia Yes.

Mrs Farrow That's good.

Sonia I'm going home tomorrow and then I'm back at school.

Mrs Farrow You seem positively keen on the idea.

Sonia I am.

Mrs Farrow Not like you.

Sonia Maybe not.

Mrs Farrow Well, it's what I have come to speak to you about, Sonia. You see, I have to warn you that the school will no longer be tolerating any kind of association with drugs or street fights. Fights of any kind in fact. The punishment for either of these activities will be expulsion. Do you understand?

Sonia Yes. I agree with you, Miss.

Mrs Farrow You agree with me?

Sonia Yes.

Mrs Farrow Then what exactly did happen on Friday evening?

Alex enters, out of breath

Alex Sonia.

Sonia Alex.

Mrs Farrow Auspicious timing, Alex.

Alex Thought I'd visit Sonia, Miss, make sure she's all right.

Mrs Farrow In school hours?

Alex Sorry, Miss.

Mrs Farrow You are here now. Sonia was just about to tell me what really happened on Friday evening.

Sonia It was ——

Alex It was all those mountain bikes. Five of them. Fell right on top of you, they did. And the rack. Isn't that right, Sonia?

Mrs Farrow Thank you, Alex. I've heard it once already. Well, bike sheds it is. Goodbye, Sonia. I'm glad you are on the mend. *(To Alex)* And I'll see *you* back at school straight after lunch. Understand?

Alex Yes, Miss.

Mrs Farrow exits

That was close.

Sonia You didn't have to do that.

Alex What?

Sonia Tell her all that stuff about the bikes. I was going to tell her the truth.

Alex What would you want to do that for?

Sonia I could say it won't happen again and mean it this time.

Alex How do you know it won't happen again?

Sonia Because I am not going to have anything to do with Spider any more, or drugs.

Alex That's just because you've been in here for too long.

Sonia No, Alex, it isn't.

Alex I hear you've been talking to Spider. What did he have to say about it?

Sonia I don't care what Spider thinks.

Alex And what about us, your mates?

Sonia gives no answer

Are you giving us up as well?

Sonia gives no answer

Carrot was right. You have changed.

Sonia Only for the better. And no, I'm not giving up my mates.

Alex Good, because we're fighting Pinch's gang on Friday. He wants to challenge your leadership. Will you be well enough?

Sonia I'm not fighting any more.

Alex You can't just not fight, Sonny, you'll get beaten up. Look what happened last time.

Sonia Yes. Look what happened last time. I don't want all this rubbish in my life. It doesn't have to be like this. I don't want drugs, or power, or leadership. I just what to find out what I really enjoy doing and do it. If someone tries to beat me up then I'll defend myself as best I can, but I don't *want* to fight. I don't want to go on living the life I've been living. People may try and stop me from changing and accuse me of deserting them, but I'm not really. I just don't want it to be like it has been. It nearly killed me last time, so what have I got to lose? If the gang wants to join me then I'll be happy. That's what I really want. But if you want to carry on as we were before, then you can do it without me.

Pause

Alex is silent. He starts to cry

Alex I can't believe you nearly died. I was so scared.(*He pauses*) I thought I might not see you again.(*He pauses*) I don't know what's happening. Everything's changing.

Sonia It will be all right, Alex.

Alex stops crying

Alex (*wiping his eyes*) You dare tell anyone I cried! Anyway, I bought you a magazine. And I haven't asked how you are feeling?

Sonia Well, it's strange but I'm feeling alive. Very much alive.

Scene 8

It is the end of the school day

School children cross the stage in various directions

Alex enters and walks purposefully, deep in thought. He sits down

Debbie enters

Debbie Hey Alex. I was expecting you back at lunchtime what happened?
Alex I needed to think.

Carrot and Spud enter and join Alex and Debbie. Carrot carries a school bag

Debbie Is she OK?
Alex She's fine. Different.
Carrot I told you.

Spider and a thug enter

Spider Look what I've found, a bunch of spineless cowards.
Alex Go to hell, Spider.

Mrs Farrow approaches them

Spider is angry and moves towards Alex aggressively. The thug notices Mrs Farrow and stops Spider

Spider and the thug leave

Mrs Farrow It's no good turning up now, we've broken up for the day.
Alex I needed to think.
Mrs Farrow That is what school is for, Alex.
Alex Yes, Miss.

Mrs Farrow exits

Carrot Do you see what I mean now?

Alex It puts things in perspective seeing her in hospital. She's let go of the things she used to want. She doesn't want to do drugs. She doesn't want to fight. She's given up her drive to prove something. And it's like she's — lighter.

Carrot Does she want to leave the gang?

Alex Possibly.

Debbie And you?

Alex Well, it's as though I've been drifting on a massive ocean with only the side of a little wooden boat to hang on to. I'm holding on to it for dear life, terrified to let go in case I drown and sink to the bottom. But if I look again closely, it's not a boat on the ocean I'm holding on to after all. It's a wreck and it's lying on the sea bed. I've been keeping myself under all this time. If I let go I'll float up to the surface and breathe and swim to whereever I want to swim to.

Debbie Alex.

Alex I thought the gang was a safe place to be. I could be an important member of the group. If I went around on my own, it would look as though there was something wrong with me. But I'm not happy. It's holding me back. I want to let go and not worry so much about what other people will think.

Spud Are you going to leave the gang?

Debbie There won't be a gang left.

Spud Then what will I do?

Alex Why are you in the gang, Spud? Why are you so sure you need it?

Spud Because you're my mates. Because I like doing the things you like doing.

Alex No I mean, why do you like us? Why do you like doing the things you like doing?

Spud I don't know.

Alex No idea?

Spud I do have an idea, but I just don't want to say it.

Alex Spider's right, we are a bunch of cowards.

Carrot I'm not a coward.

Debbie Nor am I.

Spud Nor am I.

Alex OK then. We'll play a truth game.

Spud No way, I'm not playing that.

Alex You see. We'd rather not think about it.

Debbie Sonia's decided she doesn't need the gang any more. Alex has decided he doesn't need the gang any more. There isn't really a gang left, so we might as well ask ourselves why the gang is so important to us.

Carrot We could all write it down instead of saying it. Put the bits of paper in here —(*he points to his cap*) and then read them out. (*He starts to take out a pencil case and paper from his bag*)

Debbie So that no-one else knows who wrote it?

Carrot Yeah.

Alex Carrot, you're a genius.

They distribute paper and the pens from the pencil case

Spud I don't know about this.

During the following they start to write their entries onto paper

Spud I don't know what to put.

Debbie Put the truth.

At this point in the play each performer needs to write their character a short soliloquy that reveals what they are thinking— Why did they join the gang? How is it effecting them now? What would they like to change? And so on

During the following, when a character is speaking his/her innermost thoughts the main light dims and a gentle spotlight focuses on the speaker. The lights return to normal between the soliloquies

A gentle spotlight comes up on Spud

Spud The truth. Why should I tell them, they'll probably only laugh. The truth is ...(soliloquy)
Carrot Do we put why we were in the gang before or why we want to be in the gang now?
Debbie Just write it.
Carrot How do you spell ... Oh no, it doesn't matter.

A gentle spotlight come up on Carrot

Carrot (*soliloquy ...*)
Alex Hurry up.
Debbie You can't have finished already.

A gentle spotlight comes up on Debbie

Debbie (*soliloquy...*)

A gentle spotlight comes up on Alex

Alex (*soliloquy...*)
Carrot All right. There.

Carrot hands around his cap. They all fold their bits of paper and put them in

   Ready? Debs, you go first.

Debbie takes a piece of paper and reads

The following dialogue they have written down can be changed. The performers may want to decide what their character wrote down

Debbie (*reading*)"I wanted to be a member of the gang, because I

thought that if I went around on my own it would look as though
there was something wrong with me."

Spud I know who wrote that one.

Debbie Spud! (*reading*) "Sometimes, I don't really want to do what
you lot are doing, but I do it anyway to be part of the gang."

Carrot Next.

Alex takes one

Alex (*reading*) "Sometimes I like doing things just because they
worry my Dad. He's always threatening to leave us, so I do things
to worry him deliberately so that he'll stay." (*To Debbie*) I didn't
know that

Carrot Spud.

Spud takes one

Spud I can't read this one. It's my own.

Carrot Go on.

Spud No! (*She swaps it for the other one in the hat*)

Carrot We'll know whose that one is now.

Spud Sh. (*Reading*) "I like being in the gang, but I quite often feel
that I'm not allowed to do what I really want to do. Like, I don't
really want to fight but I join in because it's the done thing. I like
it when we do drugs, but sometimes I wonder if the risks are worth
it."

Carrot Right. Last one. Can't imagine who wrote this one.

Spud Shut up. (*She hides her face*)

Carrot (*reading*) "Everyone always says I'm the stupid one, but
when I'm in the gang I can prove that I'm not."

Alex Wasn't that bad, was it?

Spud I suppose not.

Debbie I think I learned something.

Spud What's that?

Debbie We've stopped enjoying ourselves.

Carrot I don't want to fight Pinch's gang anymore.

Spud Nor do I.
Debbie Nor do I.
Alex Then we won't. We'll tell them we're not a gang any more.
We are just a group of friends.

Scene 9

*Spider sits on a gym bench and lifts an arm weight. Two thugs stand
either side. One stands behind him holding a towel*

Spider Forty-eight. Forty-nine. Fifty. Phew!

*The thug mops Spider's brow with the towel and starts giving him
a shoulder massage*

Ow!
Thug You're getting tenser every day.
Spider Hardly surprising. I'm plagued with misfortune. Business
is bad. Very bad. Dingo is working his way round all the schools.
Sonny claims to have given up drugs, gone straight. "I'm clean,
I'm cleansed," she says. "I don't want power," she says. "I had a
dream about a net". What am I supposed to make of it all.
Nobody's buying from me any more. I'm on my way out.
Thug Don't worry so much, Spider. Relax. You're just feeling
paranoid because of that stuff you took last night. Son'll come
around. Everything will get back to normal again.
Spider You heard how Alex spoke to me. No, it's gone around the
school already that Son is going through her weirdo change.
They'll all lean her way and then that'll be it. I can feel it. "No
thanks, Spider." "Not today thank you, Spider." "We're all clean
now, cleansed."
Thug You could always go into real estate. I've got a cousin in real
estate. He makes thousands. He's got a flat and a car ——
Spider Jimbo?
Thug Yes, boss?
Spider Shut it.

Thug Sorry, boss.

Spider Leave me alone. I want to be alone.

Thug Shall we come back later?

Spider No. I won't be here. I'm going out. (*Throwing his towel at them*) Well, go on then!

The thugs exit

Scene 10

Sonia's house

Margaret is arranging some roses in a vase. Peter is restless. He is looking through a newspaper, but cannot concentrate

Peter It's no good. I can't concentrate. Is she in?

Margaret She's not back from school yet. She said she was going to try out for the netball team tonight.

Peter A likely story. Yesterday, it was the school choir and now the netball team. She's only been back at school for two days. What is she doing? Making up for all the lost years?

Margaret She's changed, Peter.

Peter I don't believe it.

Margaret People do, you know.

Peter That girl has really messed things up for me. You should see the way they look at me at the station. With pity in their eyes. There is nothing more humiliating than pity.

Margaret You are good at your job and that's what counts.

Peter I thought we had set her a good example. Taught her the law; what was right and what was wrong. So what happened?

Margaret She's young. She's growing up. Give her time. She'll give you a reason to be proud of her yet.

Peter I doubt it.

Margaret Have patience. The main thing is she is well again. That's what counts and now we can enjoy some peace and quiet.

Peter While it lasts, Margaret, while it lasts.

SCENE 11

An old boatyard. It is early evening

The lighting is dim. An owl hoots

The Harwood gang enter from one side. The King Edward's gang enter from the other side. They stand facing each other. Spud and Sonia are absent

Carrot Hallo, Spice.
Spice Hallo, Carrot.
Carrot How are you?
Spice I'm fine thanks.
Pinch Where is your leader?
Alex She's not here.
Pinch I can see that.
Debbie We don't want to fight.
Pinch Oh, so you don't want to fight.

In pairs they begin to circle each other

   You agree that I'll be the leader then?
Debbie We don't want to be led either.
Loraine Then who's going to lead?
Pinch There has got to be a leader. Then everybody knows whose got the power.
Debbie What's so great about power?
Carrot Yeah. What good has it been doing anybody?
Loraine It gets you what you want.
Debbie Like?
Tufty Don't be stupid.
Pinch We just want everyone to know that we can't be walked on.
Tufty Yeah.
Spice Or pushed around, or picked on, or bullied!
Debbie But we're not going to do that.

Loraine Yeah right! How do we know this isn't a trick to get us to Harwood unprepared for all the attitude we're going to get.

Debbie You'll have to trust us.

Loraine Too risky.

Pinch Fighting for power now would solve things once and for all.

Tufty Yeah.

Alex Look, if there is any bullying, we could help each other out.

Carrot Join forces.

Spice It's worth considering, Pinch.

Pinch No, tell Sonia I'll fight her alone if I have to. One of us is going to rule Harwood.

Spud runs on, out of breath

Carrot Spud!

Spice I just saw Dingo and Spider outside King Ed's. They've gone into partnership. I heard Dingo talking about wanting more weight in the schools — *(to Pinch)* — and I saw them talking to your little brother.

Pinch Jamie?

Spice Yeah. They were telling him to meet them later.

Pinch Not Jamie. Jamie wouldn't ——

Spice I saw them.

Pinch No.

Pinch and his gang run out to look for Jamie

Spud *(shouting after them)*They were by the smoker's tree.

SCENE 12

Pinch is sitting alone on a bench

Sonia enters with the child in white

Pinch turns his back on Sonia, when he sees her. During the following, his tone is highly sarcastic

Sonia Pinch! I've been looking for you. How's Jamie?

Pinch He's sick. Very sick.

Sonia What did he take?

Pinch Oh, how sweet. Are you really worried?

Sonia I want to help you.

Pinch You want to help me? Since when did you think of anyone but yourself.

Sonia Look. I came to make you a proposition.

Pinch Go and tell someone who cares.

Sonia I thought we could set up Spider and Dingo. Arrange a deal in full view of the police. My Dad's a policeman.

Pinch Everyone know's that. It's the big joke.

Sonia So what do you think? We could get the two youngest to do it? Spud and Spice.

Pause

Pinch doesn't answer

I don't think you care about your brother.

Pinch What? I don't care? He didn't know where he was or what he was doing. He thought he was going to die. I spent hours trying to persuade him he was going to be all right. He's been in bed for two days. I can't think about anything else.

Pause

Sonia So? Are you interested?

Pinch doesn't answer

Well, we are going to do it anyway.

Sonia walks away

Pinch (*calling after her*) When?

Sonia Tonight. In the park. Eight o'clock. I might see you there then.

Pinch doesn't answer

Sonia and the child exit

SCENE 13

Dingo and Spider wait for their customers to arrive

Dingo They are late.

Spider This seems to be working out though, Dingo. The two of us. I've always wanted to go into partnership.

Dingo Where are they?

Spider Partnership. Sounds impressive doesn't it? Part-ner-ship. The thing that I've always liked about you, Dingo, is that you think. Like me, you are a thinker. You know, it was just the other day, as I was ironing my socks, that it suddenly struck me ...

Spud and Spice enter

Dingo About time.

Spider Spud and Spice? What are you two doing together?

Spud Can't stay enemies forever, you know.

Dingo Just give me the money.

Spud Give him the money, Spice.

Spice hands Spider the money and Spider hands Spice the drugs. Dingo immediately snatches the money from Spider

As soon as the transaction has been made Spud and Spice run off. Peter approaches with the police

Spider and Dingo are arrested and handcuffed

Dingo What's going on.

Spider Get off me you ...

Policeman I am arresting you on suspicion of supplying a controlled drug. You do not have to say anything, but it may harm your defence if you do not mention when questioned something which you later rely on in court. Anything you do say may be given in evidence.

Spider What did he say?

Policeman You're nicked!

Dingo You haven't got anything on us.

The Policemen pulls out packets from Spider's and Dingo's pockets

Peter Haven't we?

The policemen start to take Dingo and Spider away

Spider I want a lawyer.

They exit, as Sonia and the child enter

Peter We've been wanting these two for ages.

Sonia You were great, Dad.

One of the policemen enters

Policeman We are taking them in now.

Peter Yes, I won't be long. This is my daughter, Sonia.

Policeman Pleased to meet you, Sonia. (*Turning to Peter*) See you at the station.

The policemen exits

Peter and Sonia are alone on stage. Peter walks around awkwardly looking for the right thing to say

Peter Listen, I've been meaning to talk to you — um ... You see — when I was a young lad — it was quite different then — and — um — I remember when your mother first told me ... No — er ... You see, when you said that Dingo and ... Look, what I am trying to say is that I'm proud of you.

Sonia Really?

Peter Yes. (*There is an awkward moment when he doesn't know what else to say and gets embarrassed*) Right that's it. I'll see you later. (*Turns to go*)

Sonia Bye, Dad.

Peter (*turning back*) Goodbye, Sonia. You're a good sort.

Peter exits. Sonia's gang and Pinch's gang enter

Tufty Did you see the look on Spider's face?

Loraine He was livid.

Pinch Good!

Sonia We won't be hearing from those two again.

Pinch Yeah well, thanks for … You know.

Sonia It was nothing. My Dad's been waiting for a chance to charge those two for ages. He wouldn't believe that I wasn't mixed up with them still. We've done each other a favour. I hope we can be friends.

Alex So, what are we going to do now? Join forces or fight?

Spice I'm for joining forces.

Carrot Me too.

Debbie All those in favour of joining forces raise your hand.

Carrot and Spice put their hands straight up. Alex and Sonia follow. Then Debbie. Tufty and Loraine look at Pinch to see what he is going to do. Eventually he raises his hand and Tufty and Loraine follow

Carrot Yes!

Spice Hooray.

Carrot and Spice are very happy with the decision. Everyone notices. Carrot and Spice then try to look cool and indifferent. But during the following conversation Carrot slyly makes his way over to Spice

Alex That settles it then.

Pinch But, I refuse to be called the Harwood gang.

Spud Well think of a new name. (*She turns to the audience and imagines the new gang name lit up in lights*) What about *The Animals*.

Carrot In case you hadn't noticed, Spud, there has already been a group called *The Animals*. A pop group.

Tufty When that policeman pushed past us with Spider he touched my hair. Look. It's all messed up.

Loraine You'll live.

Spice steps forward and imagines a new gang name lit up in lights

Spice What about *The Monkees* then?
Sonia *The Monkees*?
Loraine Yuk!
Carrot There's already been a group called *The Monkees* too.
Tufty Yeah. Stupid!
Spud (*to herself*) Think!
Tufty I've got it. I've got it.
Everybody What?
Tufty This one has great potential
Debbie What?
Tufty (*imagining the new name up in lights*) The Beatles.
Everyone Tufty!

They exit, talking amongst themselves

Music comes in as they leave. Suggestions are: "Free" by Stevie Wonder, "Feeling Good" by Nina Simone, "Free" by George Michael

A spotlight comes up

The child in white steps forward into the spotlight as the main light dims. She smiles and waves to the audience

Black-out

THE END

FURNITURE AND PROPERTY LIST

SCENE 1

On stage: Single hospital bed
Bedside table. *On it*: glass of water
Bedside chair

Off stage: 3 torches (**Spider and thugs**)

SCENE 2

On stage: As SCENE 1
Doctor's notes on a clipboard

Personal: **Nurse**: pills

SCENE 3

On stage: Teacher's desk and chairs

SCENE 4

On stage: As SCENE 1

Off stage: Box of ginger biscuits (**Margaret**)

SCENE 5

On stage: *No props*

SCENE 6

On stage: *No props*

SCENE 7

On stage: As SCENE 1

SCENE 8

On stage: *No props*

Off stage: Bag containing a pencil case and paper. Pencil case contains
                pens (**Carrot**)

Personal: **Carrot**: Cap

SCENE 9

On stage: Gym bench
                Arm weight
                Towel

SCENE 10

On stage: Roses in a vase for **Margaret**
                Newspaper for **Peter**

SCENE 11

On stage: *No props*

SCENE 12

On stage: Bench

SCENE 13

On stage: *No props*

Off stage: Money (**Spice**)
                Drugs (**Spider**)

Personal: **Policeman**: handcuffs
                Spider: packets of drugs
                Dingo: packets of drugs

LIGHTING PLOT

Practical fittings required: Nil

Scene 3

To open: General interior lighting

No cues

Scene 4

To open: General interior lighting.
             Light through window DS

Cue 7   **Sonia**: " I remember my dream now"   (Page 13)
             Fade main lights a little
             Bring up spot on **Sonia**

Cue 8   **Spider**: "Have you lost it?"   (Page 14)
             Restore main lights; cut spot

Cue 9   **Margaret** switches of the light   (Page 18)
             Cut general interior light
             Light from window floods into the room

Scene 5

To open: General exterior lighting

No cues

Scene 6

To open: General exterior lighting

No cues

Scene 7

To open: General interior lighting
             Light through window DS

No cues

SCENE 8

To open: General exterior lighting

Cue 10:   **Debbie**: "Put the Truth."   (Page 28)
Dim main lights
Bring up gentle spotlight on **Spud**

Cue 11:   End of **Spud**'s soliloquy   (Page 29)
Cut spotlight, restore main lights

Cue 12:   **Carrot**: "... it doesn't matter."   (Page 29)
Dim main light
Bring up gentle spotlight on **Carrot**

Cue 13:   End of **Carrot**'s soliloquy   (Page 29)
Cut spotlight, restore main lights

Cue 14:   **Debbie**: "... finished already."   (Page 29)
Dim main lights
Bring up gentle spotlight on **Debbie**

Cue 15:   End of **Debbie**'s soliloquy   (Page 29)
Cut spotlight on **Debbie**
Bring up gentle spotlight on **Alex**

Cue 16:   End of **Alex**'s soliloquy   (Page 29)
Cut spotlight, restore main lights

SCENE 9

To open: General interior lighting

No cues

SCENE 10

To open: General interior lighting

No cues

SCENE 11

To open: Dim evening lighting

No cues

SCENE 12

To open: General interior lighting

No cues

SCENE 13

To open: General exterior lighting

Cue 17:	Music plays *Bring up spotlight*	(Page 39)
Cue 18:	**Child** steps into the spotlight *Dim main lights*	(Page 39)
Cue 19:	**Child** waves to the audience *Black-out*	(Page 39)

EFFECTS PLOT

To open: Techno music

Cue 1   **Spider** exits   (Page 1)
                  Fade Techno music
                  Bring up heartbeat sound. Mix with the faint
                  sound of an ambulance

Cue 2   Interior lights come up on SCENE 2   (Page 2)
                  Fade sound of heartbeat

Cue 3   **Sonia**: " Sh. Listen."   (Page 14)
                  The sound of a fiddle being played

Cue 4   **Spider**: " ... bleeding window."   (Page 15)
                  Cut sound of the fiddle

Cue 5   **Everybody** exits   (Page 39)
                  Music comes in
                  Suggestions "Free" by Stevie Wonder
                  "Feeling Good" by Nina Simone
                  " Free" by George Michael